STAR WARS® TALES

Volume 3

DARK HORSE COMICS®

STAR WARS TALES

CONTENTS

Publisher / Mike Richardson
Editor / Dave Land
Assistant Editor / Philip Simon
Collection Designer / Lia Ribacchi
Art Director / Mark Cox

Special thanks to
Chris Cerasi and Lucy Autrey Wilson
at Lucas Licensing

STAR WARS®: TALES — VOLUME 3

This book collects issues 9 through 12 of the Dark Horse
quarterly comic-book anthology *Star Wars®: Tales*.

Dark Horse Comics, Inc.
10956 SE Main Street
Milwaukie, OR 97222

www.darkhorse.com

Comic Shop Locator Service: (888) 266-4226

First edition: January 2003
ISBN: 1-56971-836-9

1 3 5 7 9 10 8 6 4 2
Printed in China

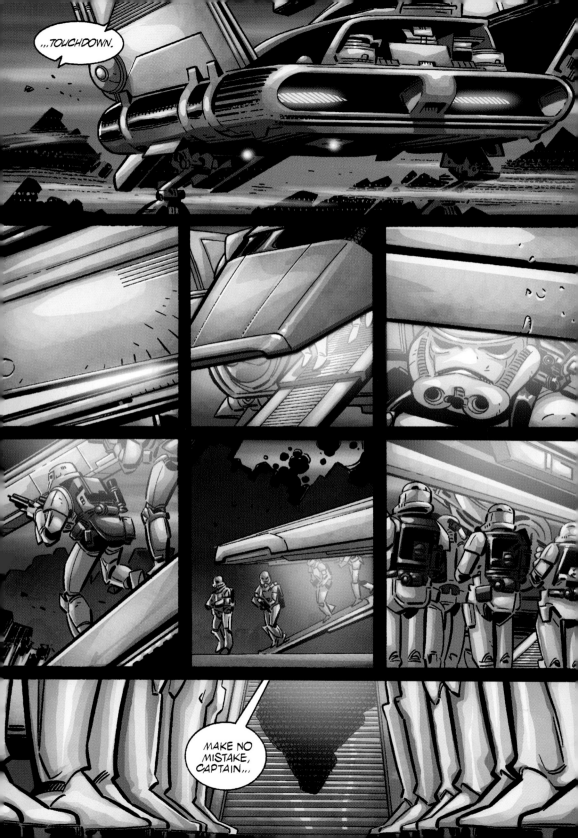

I DON'T NEED HELP TO DESTROY AN IMPOSTER.

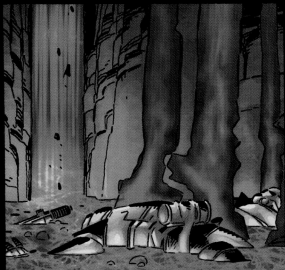

IT'S YOU WHO WEARS THE MASK...

...YOU WHO HIDES HIS UN-WORTHINESS, TELL ME...

...WHICH OF US IS TRULY AN IMPOSTER?

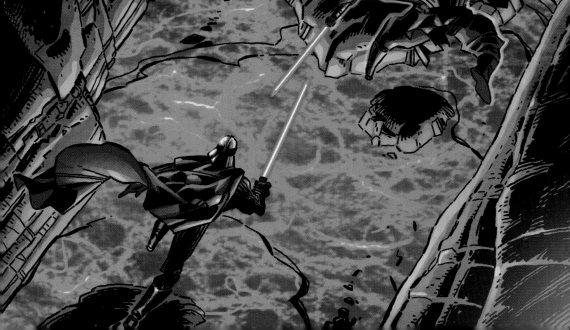

"INTRIGUING..."

"...THEY ARE MORE EVENLY MATCHED THAN WE SUSPECTED.

BUT MAUL WILL BE VICTORIOUS.

HE IS AN ENGINE OF PURE HATE. THIS OTHER...

KZICH

"...THERE'S TOO MUCH OF THE LIGHT IN HIM."

RRRRRMMMMBLL

ATLERIA.

THE **STONE RUINS** HAVE LAIN AS SILENT AS THE REST OF THIS **FORSAKEN** WORLD FOR AN AGE.

IT'S PEOPLE HAVING **LONG SINCE** ABANDONED THEIR DYING PLANET FOR THE **SANCTUARY** OF **NEIGHBORING WORLDS.**

T IS THIS **PROXIMITY** TO THRIVING COLONIES THAT AS ATTRACTED A **NEW KIND** OF INHABITANT... NE THAT **TRULY APPRECIATES** THE SECRETIVE OVER OFFERED BY **FOG** AND **DARKNESS**...

AREA SIX IS SECURE. OVER.

... LITTLE DO THEY SUSPECT THAT AS OF THIS MINUTE -- **THAT COVER IS BLOWN.'**

LOOKS LIKE OUR **INFORMANT** WAS BEING CANDID, TEAM ...

... WE MOST **DEFINITELY** HAVE THE BEGINNINGS OF A **ECRET IMPERIAL BASE** OVER HERE !

WHAT'S THE **PLAN,** CHIEF?

TO **STOP** THEM, OF COURSE.

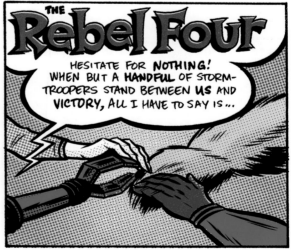

THE **Rebel Four**

HESITATE FOR **NOTHING!** WHEN BUT A **HANDFUL** OF STORM-TROOPERS STAND BETWEEN **US** AND **VICTORY,** ALL I HAVE TO SAY IS...

...IT'S REBELLIN' TIME!

FALAEM ONN

GRIMGRIM

F4-MF

SOO RCHARRZ

IN A BLAZE OF DYNAMIC ACTION, FOUR BRAVE FREEDOM FIGHTERS STORM THE WOULD-BE STRONGHOLD...

...AND WOE TO THOSE WHO STAND BEFORE THEM!

HOWEVER... COLD, MALEVOLENT EYES SURVEY THE SCENE FROM BUT A SHORT DISTANCE AWAY.

FOOLS.

THE DARK SIDE OF THE FORCE RENDERS ONE SUCH AS MYSELF IMMUNE TO SURPRISE.

PITY THE SAME CAN NOT BE SAID OF YOU...

HIS FOES VANQUISHED, **DARTH VADER** SEEMS STRANGELY **DISTANT**...

SIGH.

THESE **PATHETIC** REBELS ARE NO MATCH FOR THE **POWER** OF THE **DARK SIDE**.

I **CRAVE** A **WORTHY OPPONENT!** I DESIRE TO FACE **JEDI** WITH LIGHTSABER IN HAND **ONCE MORE**--!

SURELY YOU **JEST**, LORD VADER.

A **SWIFT DEFEAT** SUCH AS THIS IS SOMETHING THE **EMPIRE** CAN BE **PROUD** OF~

ACCKKK!

CHOKE!

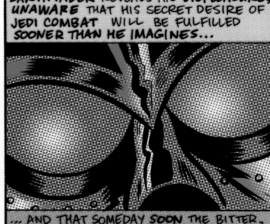

DARTH VADER REVEALS HIS **DISPLEASURE,** UNAWARE THAT HIS SECRET DESIRE OF JEDI COMBAT WILL BE FULFILLED SOONER THAN HE IMAGINES...

... AND THAT SOMEDAY SOON THE BITTER, TWISTED MAN CALLED **DARTH VADER** SHALL FINALLY BE AT **PEACE**.

A MASH NOTE FOR 1977. XO Jay Zo

PLEASE.
PLEASE.
PLEASE.
DON'T LET ME BE PICKED TO GO IN FIRST.
TROOPER

THAT'S MY PRAYER, TO ANYONE WHO'LL HEAR IT.

EVERY SINGLE TIME WE DO THIS JOB.

AND I'VE DONE DOZENS.

I CAN'T SEE OUR LASERS CLAWING FOR THE REBEL SHIP, OR THEIR RETURN FIRE SPARKING OFF OUR HULL, OR THE HIT THEY TAKE IN THE DRIVES THAT LEAVES THEM CRIPPLED--

DON'T NEED TO SEE, BECAUSE THAT'S WHAT ALWAYS HAPPENS-- BECAUSE *NO ONE* OUTRUNS A STAR DESTROYER--

BUT NOW IT'S DOWN TO US. THE BOARDING PARTY.

AND THE MAN WHO'S PICKED TO GO IN FIRST GETS BLASTED.

AND EVERY TIME I PRAY IT WON'T BE ME.

GREATER MARIANAS.

THE HOLE WHERE I WAS BORN.

PA HAD WORKED THE GRIT FOR FORTY YEARS, AN OLD-TIME YAGGIE MAN. ATE THEIR MEAT AND WORE THEIR HIDES, AND TRADED THEM FOR GAS SO HE COULD KEEP ON SPEARING MORE...

EVERY MAN IS BORN THE SAME, SON. A SENTIENT BEIN', LIVIN' FREE BENEATH THE STARS.

NO MATTER HOW RICH OR POOR HE GROWS TO BE, THAT RIGHT THERE IS THE LAST THING YOU CAN TAKE FROM HIM--

AN' ANYONE WHO'D TRY, THEY'RE THE LOWEST TRASH THERE IS.

ON A GOOD DAY, I'D ONLY HEAR THAT TWICE.

WHAT'S ALL THIS?

IN THE NAME OF HIS EXALTED HIGHNESS EMPEROR PALPATINE, GREATER MARIANAS IS HEREBY PROCLAIMED TO BE UNDER THE PROTECTION OF THE EMPIRE...

PROTECTION FROM WHAT?

THEY'VE HEARD OF US ON CORUSCANT?

IMPERIAL TAX IS EIGHTY-FIVE PERCENT, SOME SAY...

SHUT UP!

THERE'LL BE NO PERMANENT GARRISON HERE, FOR WHICH I'M SURE WE'RE ALL GRATEFUL! REVENUE WILL BE GATHERED AT MID AND END OF SEASON!

DON'T GIVE US CAUSE TO NOTICE YOU! THAT IS ALL!

WHAT IF WE DON'T WANT TO JOIN THE EMPIRE?

DAMN RIGHT!

THEN YOU BECOME AN EXAMPLE.

EVERYTHING I'D EVER KNOWN, THOUGHT, *BELIEVED*, WAS LYING IN THE DUST WITH A LOOK NO SMARTER THAN A YAGGIE. PA HAD THE FREEDOM HE WAS BORN WITH--

THE OTHER GUY HAD A BLASTER.

AND THIS SOUNDS COLD, BUT ALL I COULD SEE WAS SOMETHING I'D NEVER EVEN DREAMED OF--

I'D LIKE TO GO WITH YOU, SIR.

YOU WANT TO JOIN THE IMPERIAL FORCES, SONNY?

Oh, WELL, YOU'D HAVE TO TAKE THE TEST...!

I DO, SIR.

YOU'D HAVE TO PROVE YOU COULD FOLLOW ORDERS, NO MATTER WHAT. HOW ABOUT EXECUTING THIS ONE-EYED SUBVERSIVE HERE?

DO YOU THINK YOU COULD DO THAT?

TO ME IT WASN'T EVIL.

IT WAS NOTHING MORE THAN COMMON SENSE.

A WAY OFF GREATER MARIANAS.

I WAS THIRD, NOT FIRST.

BY THEN IT TOOK TEN KILLS TO MAKE THE GRADE.

YOU'RE *IN!*

CLEAN UP THIS MESS AND REPORT TO THE QUARTER-MASTER! *NOW!*

AND SO IT WENT.

LEAVE HIM! *LEAVE HIM!*

LET HIM DIE AND *CLIMB!*

THE ODDS HAVE GOT TO BE AGAINST ME.

DONE THIS SO MANY TIMES, SEEN SO MANY OTHERS GO IN FIRST AND DIE, I CAN'T KEEP NOT GETTING CHOSEN--

OH, NO.

THAT'S ALL WE NEED.

THIS REBEL VESSEL IS A VITAL PRIZE, SERGEANT. YOUR MEN HAD BETTER BE UP TO THE TASK.

TH-THEY ARE, MY LORD--!

THE KID BEHIND ME MAKES A MESS IN HIS REFLEC, AND I CURSE THE DAY I EVER JOINED THE EMPIRE.

I GOT AWAY FROM GREATER MARIANAS.

I WAS FED, QUARTERED, AND EQUIPPED. HAD EVERYTHING I NEEDED. TRAVELED THE GALAXY.

SAW WORLDS I COULD NEVER HAVE IMAGINED.

SOME OF THE THINGS I DID OUT THERE...

...I GUESS I'M NOT TOO PROUD OF.

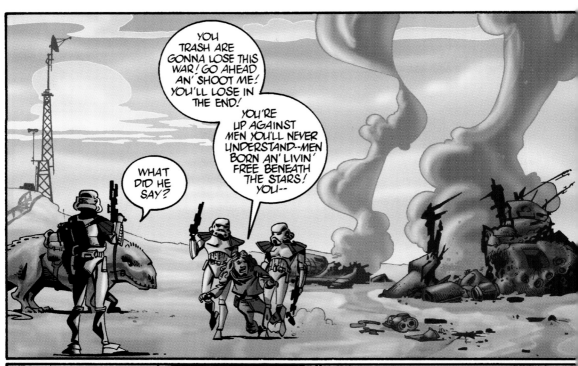

YOU TRASH ARE GONNA LOSE THIS WAR! GO AHEAD AN' SHOOT ME! YOU'LL LOSE IN THE END!

YOU'RE UP AGAINST MEN YOU'LL NEVER UNDERSTAND--MEN BORN AN' LIVIN' FREE BENEATH THE STARS! YOU--

WHAT DID HE SAY?

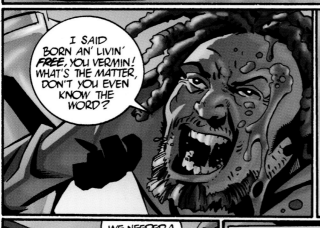

I SAID BORN AN' LIVIN' *FREE*, YOU VERMIN! WHAT'S THE MATTER, DON'T YOU EVEN KNOW THE WORD?

WE NEEDED A PRISONER--

GET ANOTHER.

LIKE THEY WOULD HAVE UNDERSTOOD. LIKE I COULD SPEAK A WORD OF THIS OUT LOUD.

LIKE ANY ONE OF THEM WOULD EVEN *DREAM* OF QUESTION-ING--

YOU!

YOU GO IN FIRST.

THE SHIP RISES IN FRONT OF US AND THE DROIDS GO STRAIGHT TO WORK.

THE OTHERS CROUCH BEHIND ME. WE'LL GO IN SHOOTING.

THE VERY INSTANT I GET HIT THEY'LL KNOCK MY FALLING CORPSE ASIDE AND START ENGAGING TARGETS, MAKING THE MOST OF THE CHANCE I'VE BOUGHT THEM.

JUST LIKE WE WERE ALWAYS TAUGHT.

I SWEAR, I SWEAR IF I SURVIVE THIS I'LL JUMP SHIP THE VERY NEXT CHANCE I GET--

I'LL CUT THE I.D. CHIPS OUT OF MY NECK AND I'LL DISAPPEAR FOREVER --

THE CHARGE IS SHAPED TO BLOW THE HATCH INWARDS, THE THEORY BEING THE DEFENDERS FLINCH AND YOU GET THAT VITAL EXTRA SECOND.

WHICH NEVER WORKS, OF COURSE.

I SWEAR I'LL LEAVE THESE BUTCHERS BEHIND FOREVER--

GO!

AND IT WORKS.

THEY FLINCH.

I GET THAT EXTRA SECOND.

BAD LUCK, *SERGEANT*--

I WENT IN FIRST AND *I'M ALIVE.*

VADER PULLS HIS DARK LORD ACT. KILLS ONE JUST TO MAKE THE POINT.

SEEN THAT A DOZEN TIMES AS WELL.

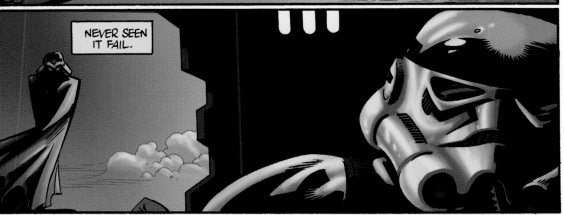

NEVER SEEN IT FAIL.

HE WANTS THE REST ALIVE, HE SAYS...I'M HARDLY EVEN LISTENING.

I'M THINKING ABOUT THAT 7IE PILOT.

ABOUT JUMPING SHIP.

ABOUT THE REBELS.

...TAMTEL SKREEJ...HERE FOR THE SKIFF GUARD OPENING...

THAT POSITION HAS BEEN FILLED. PLEASE TRY AGAIN IN 30 TO 60 DAYS.

WH--NO! WAIT! I WAS ALREADY PROMISED--

SLAM

Oh, THIS IS JUST--

...GREAT.

FUNCTIONIIIING EQUIPMENT TO THE LEFT. NONNN-FUNCTIONING EQUIPMENT TO THE RIGHT.

Eoyawa...°

Cheengan daga!°°

SERVICEABLE DROIDS THIS WAY...

° Yeah, yeah...   °° Outta the way, you idiot!

Aieee! Yadda! Yadda gah!ª

Shhh! HEY, IT'S OKAY, DON'T--

ª Agh! Rodent! Kill it!

--WAIT-A-MINUTE! THAT'S MY HAT!

'SCUSE ME, WHERE'D YOU GET THAT--

AW, NO...

YOU! WHAT'S THE BIG IDEA?!

YOU SHOULD BE HALFWAY TO BESPIN BY NOW...

YEAH, WELL, ABOUT THAT-- WHAT'S THE BIG IDEA?

KEEP IT DOWN, WILL YA? YOU GOTTA GET OUTTA HERE...

NAWNO, I WANT MY STUFF! THAT'S MY UNIFORM YOU'RE WEARING AND MY JOB YOU STOLE!

YOU HAVE ANY IDEA HOW FAR I FLEW? LET ME TELL YOU-- FAR!

HANDS OFF ME, BUCKO! AND WHERE'S ALL MY STUFF?

IT'S WAITING FOR YOU IN A NICE ROOM AT CLOUD CITY. ALL YOU GOTTA DO IS--

YOU'VE BEEN GONE FOR SOME TIME. WHY WERE YOU DELAYED? ONE ANCIENT JEDI MASTER WAS SURELY NOT BEYOND *YOUR* SKILLS.

NO, MY MASTER.

OR HAVE YOU FAILED ME?

I SIMPLY NEEDED TO EXPAND MY REPERTOIRE OF SKILLS TO BETTER SERVE YOU.

EXPLAIN THIS WEAPON.

"I HAD FOUND *SIOLO UR MANKA,* THE JEDI MASTER YOU ORDERED ME TO EXTINGUISH.

"IN THE JENTARES SYSTEM. LIT BY A WHITE DWARF STAR.

"I COULD FEEL HOW DEEPLY WRAPPED HE WAS IN A MEDITATIVE TRANCE.

"A RECLUSE FOR SEVENTY YEARS, HE RANKED AMONG THE GREATEST JEDI WARRIORS LIVING.

"BUT HE RENOUNCED THE LIGHTSABER YEARS BEFORE TO CONCENTRATE ON A PURER TECHNIQUE.

"HE SEEMED TOTALLY UNAWARE OF MY PRESENCE.

"I WAS DISAPPOINTED WITH THE EASE OF THE TASK.

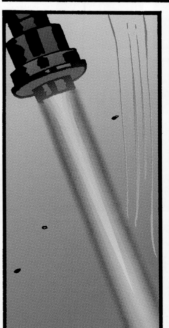

"HIS SPEED WAS SUCH THAT I BARELY SAW THE ATTACK."

"I TRIED TO FOCUS THROUGH THE PAIN, BUT TO NO AVAIL."

"IT OCCURRED TO ME THAT I SHOULD DIE. THE PRICE OF FAILURE."

"INSTEAD I RESOLVED TO *BEST* THIS ENEMY.

"I FLED.

"HE BEAT ME WITH THE SIMPLEST OF MOVEMENTS.

"HIS WEAPON, A PLAIN WOODEN STICK, WAS LONGER THAN MINE.

"HE WAS QUICKER THAN ME.

"IT WAS SIMPLE TO SEE THAT UNLESS I COULD SURPRISE HIM, HE WOULD ALWAYS WIN.

"I HAD TO GET IN CLOSE AND STRIKE BEFORE HE HAD TIME TO DEFEND.

"I SOON KNEW WHAT TO DO.

I KNEW YOU WOULD RETURN.

I'VE SEEN YOUR TYPE TOO MANY TIMES TO COUNT: ONLY VICTORY IN YOUR HEART.

NO HONOR. JUST SKILL, NO ART.

I THOUGHT YOU COMPETENT ENOUGH TO TELL FROM OUR ONE BATTLE THAT YOU CAN'T DEFEAT ME.

YOUR LAST CHANCE. FLEE.

"I'D NEVER SEEN ANYTHING MOVE THAT FAST BEFORE.

"NO POINT WAITING. I USED THE EXACT SAME ATTACK ON HIM.

A TRICK.

NO.

SIMPLY VICTORY.

IMPRESSIVE. YOU SHOULD NAME THIS WEAPON.

I FORESEE IT WILL TELL GREAT TALES.

--AN INSTRUMENT OF MURDER.

AND NAMELESS.

NO, MY MASTER. IT, LIKE MYSELF, IS NOTHING MORE THAN A TOOL IN YOUR FIST. IT IS UNDESERVING OF HONOR.

LET IT BE NOTHING MORE THAN WHAT IT IS--

EN

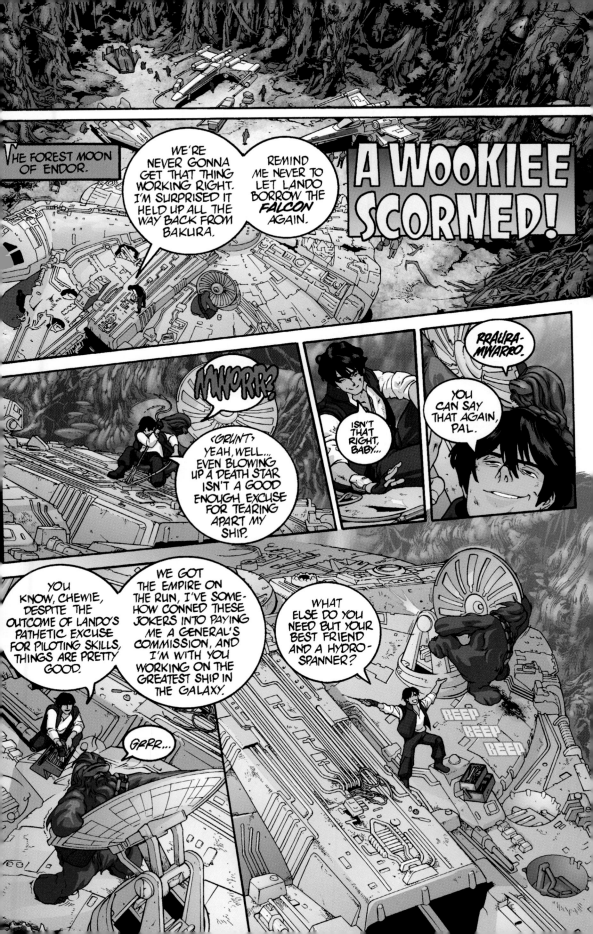

MWORR?

TRUE SPACE ROMANCE

WHAT HAPPENS WHEN YOU
GO FROM BEST FRIEND TO
BANTHA FODDER?
FIND OUT IN...

A WOOKIEE SCORNED!

I'M SO GLAD YOU DITCHED THAT WALKING CARPET FOR ME!

I KNOW, I KNOW. I GOT TOTALLY HELD UP. YOU GIVE HER AN INCH AND SHE TAKES A MILE. BUT WHAT DO YOU EXPECT FROM ROYALTY?

I MEAN, COME ON...SHE'S PRACTICALLY THE LEADER OF THE REBELLION, I GOTTA CUT HER SOME SLACK, RIGHT? I PROMISE WE'LL WORK ON THE FALCON TOMORROW, OKAY?

I PROMISE, SMUGGLER'S HONOR.

SURGRHHHZ!

BZZT BZZT BZZT

HEY, NERF HERDER.

I THOUGHT PERHAPS WE COULD CONTINUE OUR RESEARCH IN THE SURROUNDING FORESTS TOMORROW?

WELL, I WOULDN'T WANT TO LET DOWN THE SCIENTIFIC COMMUNITY.

RIGHT. AND CLEAN UP THAT FACE, FLYBOY.

FZZT

THE NEXT DAY...

HEY, CHEWIE. SORRY I'M LATE.

YOU KNOW, I'M THINKING MAYBE I'M THE ONE WHO GOT CONNED WITH THIS WHOLE GENERAL THING.

IT'S NOTHING BUT NON-STOP MEETINGS.

GROARR?

WELL, YEAH... LEIA WAS THERE. SHE'S ONE OF THE BIG WIGS, RIGHT?

I....UH... DIDN'T GET TO REALLY TALK TO HER OR ANYTHING, THOUGH.

UM... DINNER LOOKS GREAT!

MURRARRO

OH, RIGHT. SORRY. I'M SURE IT'S JUST AS GOOD COLD.

IN FACT, I'VE SORT OF GOT TO EAT IT ON THE RUN.

THE PRINCESS SHOULD BE JUST GETTING BACK FROM A QUICK RECON-NAISSANCE AND I'VE GOT TO...UH...

--DEBRIEF HER.

OH, AND I FIGURED I'D JUST TAKE HER AS CO-PILOT TOMORROW ON THAT MISSION TO ISON.

I KNEW YOU WOULDN'T MIND...IT GIVES YOU MORE TIME TO HANG OUT WITH YOUR EWOK PALS.

WURORRA RAO.

JUST WOOKIEES CUT IN HALF? IS THAT ANY WAY TO TALK ABOUT OUR LITTLE FUZZY ALLIES?

Though that "Yub-Yub" song really drives me up a wall.

ALRIGHT, PAL, CATCH YOU LATER. DON'T WAIT UP.

≑sigh≑

MORNING, PAL.

GOOD MORNING, CHEWIE!

I HOPE I HAVEN'T SAID ANYTHING TO UPSET HIM.

YOU KIDDING? HE EATS PRINCESSES LIKE YOU FOR BREAKFAST. LET'S BLOW THIS POPSICLE STAND.

HOW YOU DOING, CHEWIE?

MNNEH!

WELL, IT DOESN'T TAKE A JEDI MASTER TO SENSE THAT YOU'RE FEELING A LITTLE BIT JEALOUS. AND HEY, IT'S TOTALLY UNDERSTANDABLE. I MEAN, LEIA'S A GREAT GIRL. SHE'S SMART, STRONG, INTELLIGENT ...AND BEAUTIFUL.

I FOUND OUT SHE'S MY SISTER, YOU KNOW. EVEN WITH THE FORCE, I DIDN'T SEE THAT ONE COMING.

:sigh: TALK ABOUT A MAJOR BUMMER.

FREE MEMORY

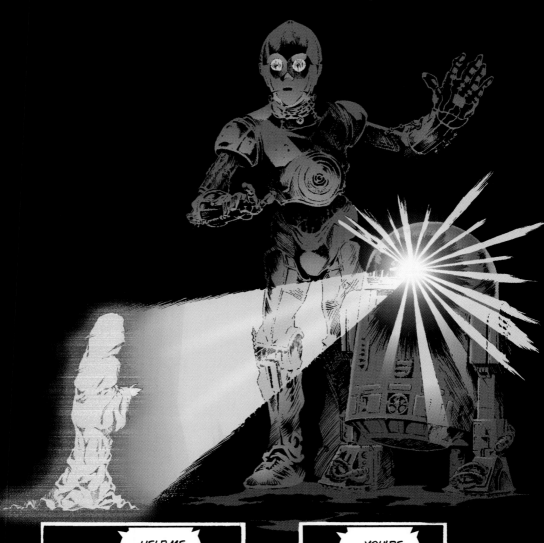

HELP ME,
OBI-WAN
KENOBI...

...YOU'RE
MY ONLY
HOPE.

3

R2-D2, WHAT IS THE MEANING OF THIS?

OF COURSE I REMEMBER IT, BUT THAT RECORDING IS ANCIENT HISTORY. DO YOU HAVE ANY IDEA HOW MUCH FREE MEMORY IT MUST BE TAKING UP IN YOUR SYSTEM? BEEDLE

IT'S EXACTLY THIS KIND OF PROBLEM THOSE NICE TECH PEOPLE WISH TO SOLVE FOR YOU. BLEET

PLAY YOUR CARDS RIGHT AND YOU JUST MAY END UP WITH A NEW MEMORY DRIVE ENTIRELY. I COULD EVEN PUT IN A WORD FOR YOU IF YOU'D BE SO--

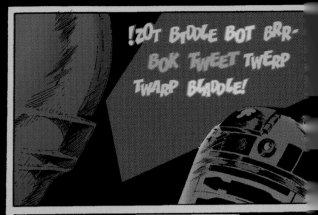

!ZOT BIDDLE BOT BRR-BOK TWEET TWERP TWARP BLADDLE!

YOU'D CERTAINLY NEVER BE MISTAKEN FOR A PROTOCOL DROID WITH LANGUAGE LIKE THAT. BOOP BEEP

HOW RUDE.

BIDDLE BIDDLE BIDDLE

OTHER RECORDING--

OH MY ...

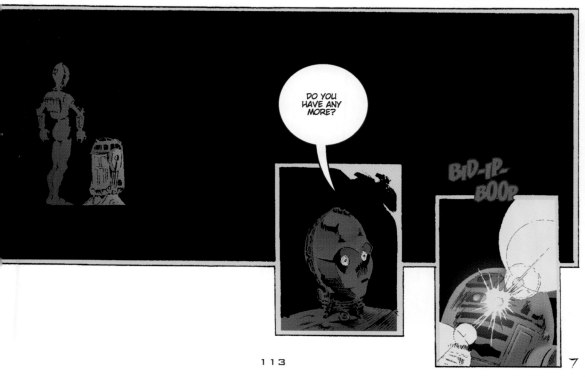

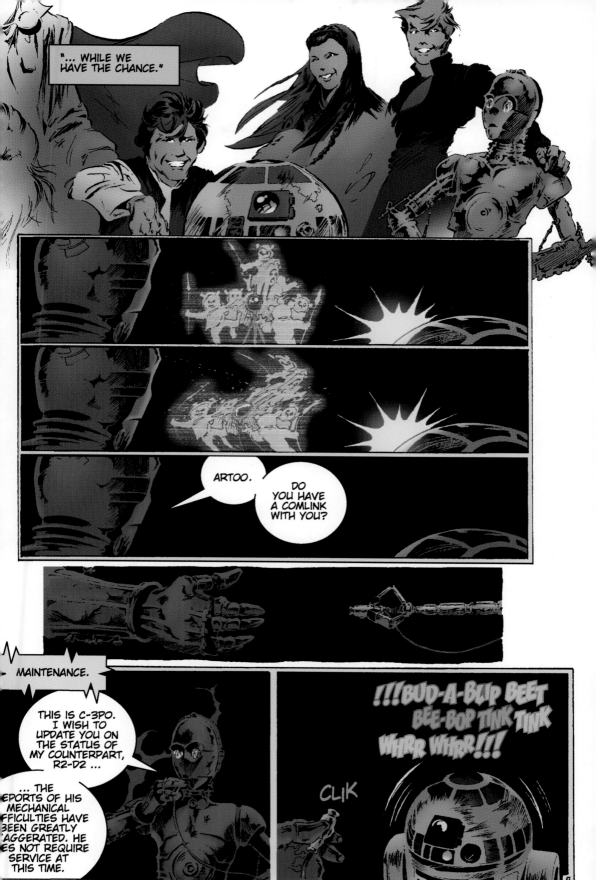

"... WHILE WE HAVE THE CHANCE."

ARTOO.

DO YOU HAVE A COMLINK WITH YOU?

MAINTENANCE.

THIS IS C-3PO. I WISH TO UPDATE YOU ON THE STATUS OF MY COUNTERPART, R2-D2 ...

... THE REPORTS OF HIS MECHANICAL DIFFICULTIES HAVE BEEN GREATLY EXAGGERATED. HE DOES NOT REQUIRE SERVICE AT THIS TIME.

!!!BUD-A-BLIP BEET BEE-BOP TINK TINK WHRR WHRR!!!

CLIK

9

THERE IS NO NEED TO HIRE BOUNTY HUNTER SCUM TO SOLVE IMPERIAL PROBLEMS.

THIS MATTER SHOULD BE HANDLED INTERNALLY.

LORD VADER, WE HAVE TRIED TO HANDLE THIS MATTER INTERNALLY AS YOU SUGGEST.

ALL OUR EFFORTS HAVE BEEN FOR NAUGHT.

IT IS A CRITICAL TIME FOR THE EMPIRE AND BRINGING IN OUTSIDE HELP IS NOTHING BUT A SIGN OF WEAKNESS.

ON THE CONTRARY. SENDING BOBA FETT AFTER THIS DESERTER SHOWS THE LENGTHS TO WHICH WE WILL GO TO MAINTAIN ORDER. THERE IS NO ESCAPING THE EMPIRE.

TREASON IS A SERIOUS CRIME AND ENLISTING FETT'S SERVICES WILL LEAVE A LASTING IMPRESSION ON OUR TROOPS.

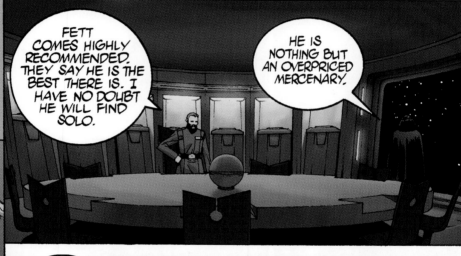

FETT COMES HIGHLY RECOMMENDED. THEY SAY HE IS THE BEST THERE IS. I HAVE NO DOUBT HE WILL FIND SOLO.

HE IS NOTHING BUT AN OVERPRICED MERCENARY.

IMPERIAL FORCES SHOULD HANDLE IMPERIAL PROBLEMS.

WE NEED A SHOW OF STRENGTH TO ILLUSTRATE THAT WE ARE NOT TO BE TRIFLED WITH.

WAM

POINT TAKEN. I WON'T CALL OFF FETT. HOWEVER, CAPTURING SOLO ON OUR OWN WOULD SEND A POWERFUL MESSAGE. SO, LORD VADER...

...WHY NOT GO AFTER HIM YOURSELF?

IF THE EMPEROR WILL ALLOW ME TO BECOME INVOLVED...

I WILL SPEAK WITH THE EMPEROR. YOU SHOULD LEAVE NOW.

FETT ALREADY HAS A HEAD START.

MINING COLONY IN THE HOTH SYSTEM.

WELL?

CAN'T I AT LEAST GET SOMETHING HOT TO DRINK?

LATER. TELL ME WHAT YOU KNOW FIRST.

" 'BOUT A MONTH BACK, A TIE FIGHTER CRASH LANDED HERE. THE PILOT SURVIVED BUT WAS IN BAD SHAPE. HE MANAGED TO WALK TO A NEARBY SETTLEMENT.

" NOT MUCH IN THE WAY OF MODERN MEDICINE OUT HERE BUT A LOCAL HEALER NURSED HIM BACK TO HEALTH.

" LAST I HEARD, HE BOARDED A TRANSPORT SHUTTLE HEADED FOR WARMER PARTS ABOUT A WEEK BACK. THINK IT WAS HEADED FOR TATOOINE..."

GO GET THAT DRINK NOW.

HOURS LATER...

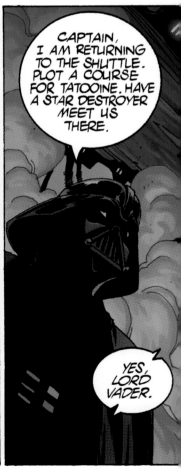

CAPTAIN, I AM RETURNING TO THE SHUTTLE. PLOT A COURSE FOR TATOOINE. HAVE A STAR DESTROYER MEET US THERE.

YES, LORD VADER.

BOOM!

133

VIIIIT

FWP

KZAK

LATER...

CAPTAIN, I WANT A FULL REPORT ON SOLO'S ESCAPE. SHIPS SIMPLY DON'T DISAPPEAR INTO NOTHING!

WE... WE'RE WORKING ON IT, LORD VADER.

BRING YOUR REPORT TO MY CHAMBERS WHEN IT IS READY. RESUME ALL NORMAL OPERATIONS AND PLOT A COURSE BACK TO THE DEATH STAR.

YES, MY LORD.

The Princess Leia Diaries

The line between the life I want to live and the life I'm expected to live is about as thin as a Hutt after a buffet.

A girl can only take so much primping and posturing. I know my father and aunts mean well, but I didn't ask to be the Princess of the Royal House of Alderaan.

There's more to the galaxy than elaborate dresses and fancy parties.

Sometimes a girl just needs her mother--especially when you're ten. Why did mine have to die?

All I have are some vague memories of a sad and beautiful woman who I'd give anything to have hugging me right now.

At the very least, she could get me out of having to learn how to behave like "a lady" --whatever that means. Personally, I'd rather be spit on by a nerf.

POISE! BALANCE! LADY-LIKE!

But instead of a mom, what do I get? My rancor of a Nanny: Madame Vesta-- tyrannical head of the "Alderaan Select Academy for Young Ladies"--

--who for some reason thinks "real ladies" can walk with books on their heads--

..and must eat as if it were a ceremony.

WHAT?!

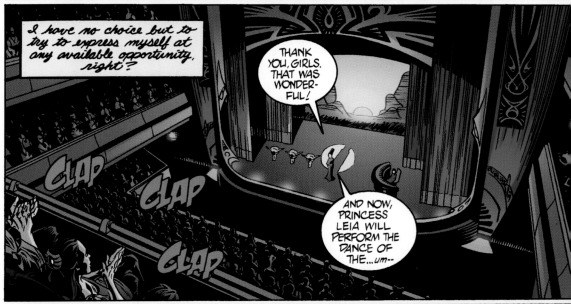

I have no choice but to try to express myself at any available opportunity, right?

THANK YOU, GIRLS. THAT WAS WONDER-FUL!

AND NOW, PRINCESS LEIA WILL PERFORM THE DANCE OF THE...um--

--TWI'LEK SLAVE GIRL. Oh, dear...

I guess I just hope in doing so, I'm not somehow disappointing my father.

CLAP   CLAP   CLAP

Well, today I had to take matters into my own hands. I can only take so much of being everyone's dress-up doll.

I certainly don't understand the obsession with hair the women around here seem to have.

YOU MUST PUT THIS ON, YOUR HIGHNESS.

IT'S SUMMER. I DON'T NEED EAR-MUFFS!

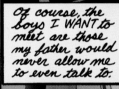

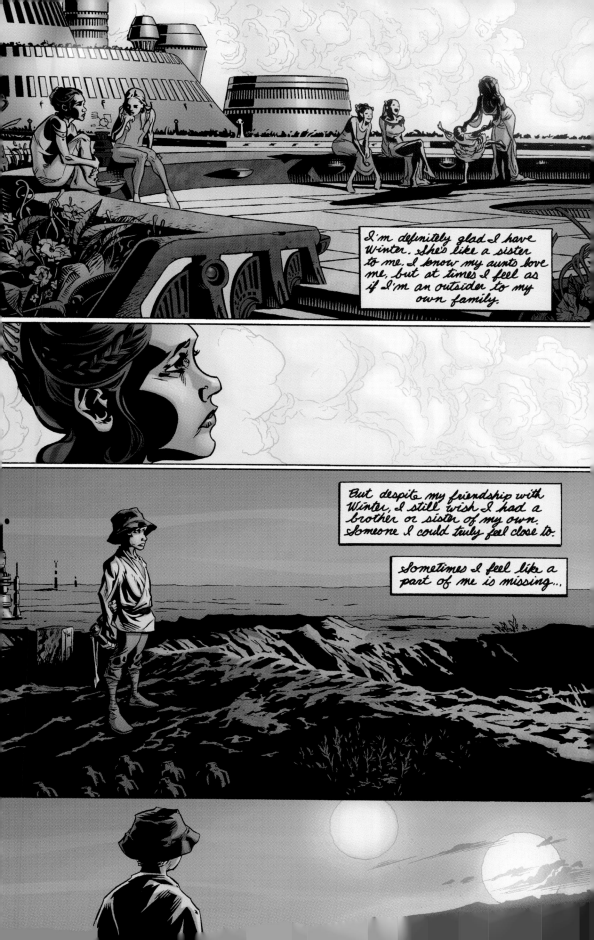

I'm definitely glad I have Winter. She's like a sister to me. I know my aunts love me, but at times I feel as if I'm an outsider to my own family.

But despite my friendship with Winter, I still wish I had a brother or sister of my own. Someone I could truly feel close to.

Sometimes I feel like a part of me is missing...

I met Governor Tarkin for the first time today.

IT'S AN um... HONOR TO HAVE YOU STOP BY, GOVERNOR TARKIN.

YES, I'M QUITE SURE. IT IS IMPORTANT TO--

I'd heard father speak of him, none of it good. I can see why.

AND WHO WAS THAT YOUNG LADY?

Oh, THAT WAS MY DAUGHTER, LEIA.

THE PRINCESS? urm. CHARMING GIRL, I'M SURE.

I'M SORRY, VICEROY.

GET A BIT OF A BEATING, DID YOU?

THIS AIN'T NOTHIN'!

YOU SHOULD SEE THE WOOKIEE!

When he looked at me, I felt like death was staring me in the eye.

I'M GROOMING HER TO TAKE MY PLACE IN THE IMPERIAL SENATE.

PERHAPS YOU SHOULD WEAN HER FIRST.

I think he represents everything that's wrong with the Empire. He even has an alien slave! Can you believe the Emperor allows slavery?!

LEIA, WHERE ARE YOU GOING?

JUST WATERING MY PLANTS.

GET ME OUT OF HERE.

What kind of galaxy do we live in?

And what can I do to change it?

CHARMING...

Well, another day, another ludicrously expensive party. I wonder how my father justifies these things when there are so many people in the galaxy who are hungry and suffering.

Shouldn't we be helping them somehow?

CAN YOU BELIEVE THAT MY SERVANT GIRL ACTUALLY WANTED TO TRY ON MY DRESS? HOW RIDICULOUS IS THAT?

PUH-LEASE!

SEEING THAT YOU COULD PROBABLY FEED HER ENTIRE FAMILY FOR A YEAR WITH WHAT IT COST...

...I BET IT WOULD HAVE MADE HER DAY.

I suppose there are all sorts of ways to handle a situation.

Oh, PLEASE. IT'S MUCH TOO GOOD FOR SOMEONE WHO WASHES MY UNDERCLOTHES.

I wonder if my ways are unfitting for a 13-year old?

My father would probably think so.

GUESS IT'S A HAND-ME-DOWN NOW.

154

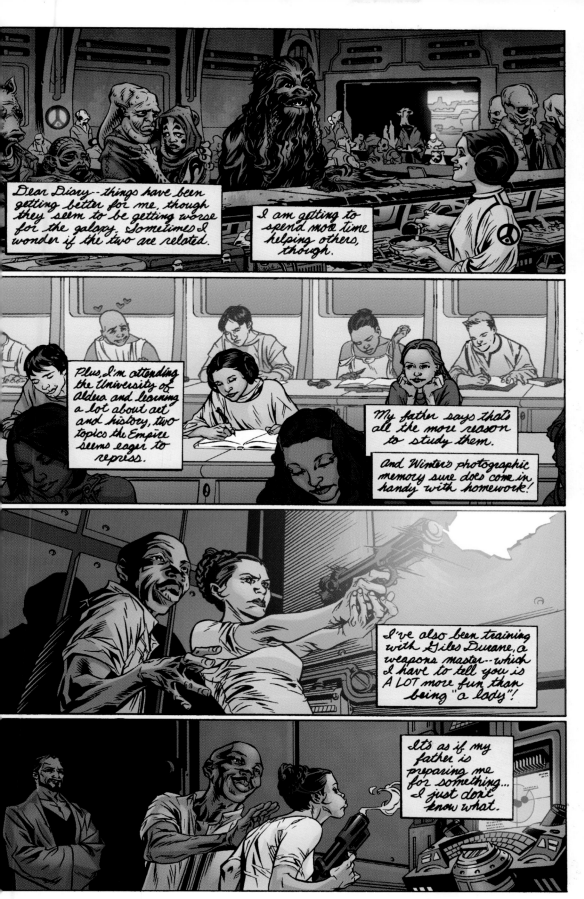

Dear Diary--things have been getting better for me, though they seem to be getting worse for the galaxy. Sometimes I wonder if the two are related.

I am getting to spend more time helping others, though.

Plus, I'm attending the University of Aldera and learning a lot about art and history, two topics the Empire seems eager to repress.

My father says that's all the more reason to study them.

And Winter's photographic memory sure does come in handy with homework!

I've also been training with Giles Durane, a weapons master--which I have to tell you is A LOT more fun than being "a lady"!

It's as if my father is preparing me for something... I just don't know what.

155

the day has finally come. My father has stepped down and I've become the youngest Senator ever to be elected...

MY LITTLE GIRL IS ALL GROWN UP.

FATHER, I WANT YOU TO KNOW I'LL DO ANYTHING I CAN TO HELP YOU WITH THE REBELLION.

HOW DO YOU KNOW ABOUT THE--

IT'S UP TO US TO MAKE A DIFFERENCE... TOGETHER.

WITH MY DIPLOMATIC IMMUNITY AND CONSULAR SHIP, I CAN RUN COVERT MISSIONS FOR THE CAUSE!

I CAN--

LEIA, LEIA... CALM DOWN. WE'LL TALK ABOUT ALL THAT LATER.

JUST KNOW NOW THAT I'M SO VERY PROUD OF YOU.

I DO, FATHER.

WAS THE SAME DAY SOLO KILLED THAT *BOUNTY HUNTER* LOWLIFE, GREEDO.

"GREEDO SHOOTS FIRST, BUT SOLO DUCKS, TAGS HIM UNDER THE TABLE . . ."

HEY-- GREEDO WAS NO *LOWLIFE.*

AND THAT BIG-SHOT *"HERO"* BLASTED HIM IN *COLD BLOOD.*

"WELL, I MEAN GREEDO WAS A RODIAN, YEAH, SO OF COURSE HE HAD COLD BLOOD, BUT . . ."

"SEE, SOLO ASKED TO MEET HIM. NOT LIKE SOLO WAS ABOVE WORKING WITH BOUNTY HUNTERS BACK THEN. PLUS, THEY WERE BOTH WORKING FOR A HUTT . . ."

"SO HE'S WAITING AT THE BAR AND SOLO COMES UP BEHIND HIM AND JUST TAKES OFF HIS HEAD."

HAN SOLO WOULDN'T'VE DONE ANYTHING LIKE THAT. THAT BOUNTY HUNTER MUST'VE DONE SOMETHING TO DESERVE IT.

YOU DIDN'T KNOW THESE GUYS.

THEY WERE *RUTHLESS*.

"THE EMPIRE HIRED ME AND A BUNCH OF GUYS TO HUNT SKYWALKER AND HIS PALS DOWN AFTER THE *BATTLE OF HOTH*.

"REMEMBER THAT--? THE REBELS GOT THEIR *BACKSIDES* HANDED TO 'EM, AND THE EMPEROR FIGURED HE COULD FINISH 'EM OFF. I ALMOST GOT 'EM, TOO.

"I TRACKED 'EM DOWN TO *KARFEDDION*. A FEW OF 'EM GOT *LOADED* IN THIS ONE CANTINA, AND I WAS GETTING READY TO CLOSE IN ON 'EM.

"THEY *TORCHED* THE WHOLE PLACE.

"*KILLED* A COUPLE DOZEN MEN, WOMEN, AND *CHILDREN*, BUT THEY DIDN'T CARE . . ."

WHAT WERE *CHILDREN* DOING IN A CANTINA?

...THEY GOT AWAY, GOT TO CLOUD CITY. THE REST IS HISTORY.

HA!

WHAT, YOU DON'T THINK I COULD TAKE SKYWALKER AND HIS GANG?

OH NO, I'M SURE YOU COULD'VE GIVEN THEM A RUN FOR THEIR MONEY.

I NEVER HEARD OF THE *FALCON* GOING TO KARFEDDION...

THE *WHAT*?

THE *MILLENNIUM FALCON*. SOLO'S *SHIP*. WON IT FROM ME ON A BET.

I'M JUST SAYING, IF THEY WERE GOING FROM HOTH TO BESPIN, WHAT WERE THEY DOING ANYWHERE NEAR KARFEDDION?

ARE YOU A PILOT?

I MEAN, IF YOU KNOW ALL THE *ROUTES* LIKE THAT. DID YOU FLY FOR THE EMPIRE, BACK IN THE DAY?

HEY, HE ASKED YOU A QUESTION.

YEAH, KID, I DID SOME FLYING. NOT THE LOCAL BULK CRUISERS, MIND YOU . . .

. . . I'M TALKING ABOUT THE BIG CORELLIAN SHIPS . . .

DIDN'T THAT *PRINCESS* DAME FIGHT HER WAY OFF A CORELLIAN, RIGHT BEFORE THEY BLEW UP THE DEATH STAR?

NO, SHE WAS *ON* THE DEATH STAR. SHE GOT AWAY BY HIJACKING ONE OF *THEIR* CORELLIANS-- THE *FALCON!*

BzzAPP

ZZKA3K

AIIIE!

SORRY ABOUT THE DROID...

I-I'M NOT SUP-P-P--

I-I'M SENATOR AMARA'S SON--

I'M NOT SUP-P-POSED TO COME TO B-B-BARS--

MY D-DAD HAS ENEMIES...

SOCCORO.

IT'S GOTTA BE HERE!

MAP I WON IN THAT SABACC GAME BETTER NOT BE BOGUS.

NEXT TIME I GET COLD, HARD CREDITS!

IF THAT OLD GEEZER DIDN'T SELL ME A LOAD OF BANTHA DUNG...

...THE MAP SAYS THE TREASURE OUGHT TO BE RIGHT AROUND...

...HERE!

SWOOP GANG!

GHOST

GET DOWN!

WHAT KINDA SPICE ARE THEY ON? A JEDI? THOSE CRAZY OLD WIZARDS ARE LONG DEAD.

MOSTLY...

YOU DON'T LOOK SO GOOD. U/h, IF YOU'RE GONNA PASS OUT OR DIE OR SOMETHING...

COULD I BORROW YOUR BLASTER? THEY'RE STILL OUT THERE...

THE FORCE WILL EASE THE PAIN.

THE FORCE, huh? YOU DON'T BELIEVE IN THAT OLD CROCK, DO YOU?

THERE IS NO TIME FOR THIS.

YOU WANT TO TELL ME WHO YOU ARE AND WHY YOU ARE HERE.

NAME'S HAN SOLO, I'M AFTER A TREASURE.

WON A MAP OFF AN OLD SPACER IN A SABACC GAME. CRAZY OLD MYNOCK THOUGHT THERE WAS A GREENFIRE GEM BURIED IN THESE RUINS.

HE TRIED TO FIND IT BUT HE NEVER COULD. BUT I KNOW I CAN.

RAH! PUNY BLASTER! PUNY HUMAN!

YOUR TIME TO MAKE THE FINAL JUMP.

SPHOW

BTEW

A Day in the Life

GIVEN WHAT I DO FOR A LIVING, I'M SURE A STRONG ARGUMENT COULD BE MADE.

ROGUES TWO AND THREE FORM UP.

I REMAIN ON THE LEADER.

COPY, WEDGE.

ON YOUR FLANK COMMANDER.

I HAVE A SHOT. REPEAT, THREE HAS A CLEAN SHOT.

NEGATIVE, THREE.

THAT FIGHTER'S SHORT-RANGE. I WANT TO SEE WHERE IT'S HEADED.

THREE DAYS.

THREE DAYS SINCE THE BATTLE OF ENDOR.

LOCK S-FOILS. PREPARE TO ENTER ATMOSPHERE.

TWO OF WHICH I ACTUALLY REMEMBER.

NOTE TO SELF--NEVER ACCEPT A DRINK FROM AN EWOK WEARING A STORMTROOPER HELMET.

I GUESS IT HASN'T SUNK IN YET.

I MEAN, WE WON, RIGHT? IT'S OVER.

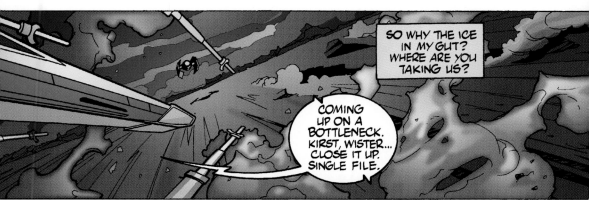

SO WHY THE ICE IN MY GUT? WHERE ARE YOU TAKING US?

COMING UP ON A BOTTLENECK. KIRST, WISTER... CLOSE IT UP. SINGLE FILE.

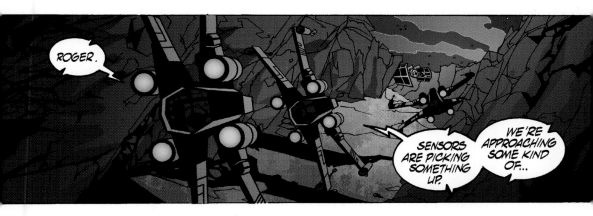

ROGER.

SENSORS ARE PICKING SOMETHING UP.

WE'RE APPROACHING SOME KIND OF...

...CLEARING, FILSWIK.

NO. NOT AGAIN.

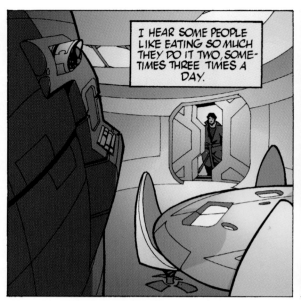

I HEAR SOME PEOPLE LIKE EATING SO MUCH THEY DO IT TWO, SOMETIMES THREE TIMES A DAY.

ACCESS DENIED. SERVING HOURS AS POSTED.

BLOW UP A COUPLE DEATH STARS, SURE, BUT TRY TO GET A SANDWICH AND...

ACCESS GRANTED.

HAN SOLO, EAT YOUR HEART OUT.

YOU MIND EXPLAINING YOURSELF COMMANDER?

189

I CAN ASSURE YOUR HIGHNESS, UNITING WITH THE REPUBLIC WILL MEAN *GREAT PROSPERITY* FOR YOUR PEOPLE.

I BELIEVE YOU ARE RIGHT, OBI-WAN KENOBI. THE JEDI ORDER HAS PROVED DEPENDABLE THESE PAST YEARS. IT IS JUST...

SOMETHING TROUBLES YOU?

IT IS MY *WIVES.* THE TEMPTATION TO EXPERIENCE THE WONDERS OF THIS WORLD IS ALIVE IN THEIR HEARTS, *hmm?*

I DO WANT THEM TO SEE IT ALL, BUT I AM ANXIOUS THEY ARE... *TOO EAGER.* I HAVE BUT *TWO* GUARDS, AND YET I HAVE *FOUR* WIVES.

I ASK YOU, THOSE I *TRUST,* TO GUARD THE TURBOLIFT, THAT I MAY SLEEP WELL, KNOWING MY WIVES WILL STAY HERE... *SAFE.*

OF COURSE. MY PADAWAN AND I GRACIOUSLY ACCEPT, KING SHA-MAR MA-DRED.

Ah! MY GRATITUDE IS ETERNALLY YOURS, KNIGHTS OF THE JEDI ORDER!

WHAT CAN WE DO TO HELP?

DRINK UP!

SHORTLY THEREAFTER, OUTSIDE THE QUARTERS OF THE KING'S WIVES...

MASTER, THE KASHIRIM MAY BE PRIMITIVE, BUT SEEM VERY WELL-MANNERED. I DON'T UNDERSTAND WHY YOU WANTED ME TO BE SO *MINDFUL.*

ANAKIN, THE KASHIRIM ARE *NOTORIOUS* THROUGHOUT THE GALAXY FOR ONE THING: *STEALING.*

A COMPETENT THIEF IS CONSIDERED A GREAT VALUE TO THEIR SOCIETY. THEY ARE JUDGED SOCIALLY BY THE ABILITY TO PILFER.

MY LIGHTSABER! IT'S *GONE!*

DON'T WORRY, NONE SLEEPS DEEPER THAN THE KING OF KASHIR.

I EXPECT YOU HAVE COME FOR YOUR WEAPON.

YOU *DID* STEAL IT.

AND FOR A *PRICE*, MAYBE IT WILL BE RETURNED TO YOU.

THAT IS... FORBIDDEN. PASSION IS FORBIDDEN.

PERHAPS THERE WOULD BE FEWER JEDI WEAPONS TO WORRY ABOUT IF THERE WAS MORE JEDI PASSION.

PERHAPS. BUT IT IS AGAINST THE JEDI CODE I AM COMMITTED TO.

BEYOND THAT, YOUR KING TRUSTS ME. I WILL NOT BETRAY HIM.

YOUR RESOLVE IMPRESSES ME.

YOU STOLE MY LIGHTSABER TO LURE ME HERE! THIS WAS A TEST?

TO MEASURE INTEGRITY? PERHAPS. I AM CERTAIN NOW MY HUSBAND, MY KING, IS WISE TO TRUST THE JEDI.

AS FOR YOUR WEAPON, I DID ENJOY STEALING IT FROM YOU.

IT IS THE WAY OF THE KASHIR.

SO... I CAN HAVE MY LIGHTSABER BACK?

I NO LONGER HAVE IT.

SOME-ONE STOLE IT AWAY FROM ME BEFORE I HAD THE CHANCE TO EVEN LOOK AT IT.

THEN CLOSE THE *WINDOW!* AND LET ME TO MY SLEEP!

I'VE SEALED IT.

NOW GO, BEFORE THE KING GROWS ANGRIER.

ЦЦЦ

CAN THIS GET ANY BETTER? THIEVES OBSESSED WITH TRUST.

MY LIGHT-SABER STILL MISSING.

WHY DIDN'T I LISTEN TO OBI-WAN? *Ughh.* HOW AM I GOING TO TELL HIM?

FWIP

KNOCK
KNOCK

ANAKIN?
ARE YOU ALL
RIGHT?

I'M FINE,
MASTER.

LISTEN,
THERE'S
SOMETHING
I MUST
TELL YOU...

...THAT
YOU LOST
YOUR
WEAPON.
I KNOW.

YOU
HAVE MY
LIGHTSABER?
BUT HOW?

I ASKED YOU TO BE ON YOUR GUARD. TO BE MINDFUL. YOU WERE NOT.

NO, MASTER.

"WHEN THE KING INTRODUCED HIS QUEENS, YOU LOST ALL FOCUS. WHILE YOU WERE DISTRACTED, ONE QUEEN EASILY STOLE YOUR LIGHTSABER..."

"...AND ONCE ASHALA HID IT IN HER ROBE..."

"...I RECLAIMED IT, USING THE FORCE."

WHY DIDN'T YOU TELL ME YOU HAD MY LIGHTSABER WHEN THE KING LEFT US?

I WANTED TO SEE HOW LONG IT WOULD TAKE YOU TO NOTICE FOR YOURSELF... AND IF YOU WOULD TELL ME.

THE KASHIRIM ARE NOT THE ONLY ONES WHO VALUE TRUST, ANAKIN. WE NEED TO TRUST EACH OTHER, TOO.

YES, MASTER.

THIS LIGHTSABER IS YOUR LIFE. DON'T LOSE IT AGAIN!

I'LL TRY NOT TO, MASTER. I PROMISE.

MASTER, THERE IS SOMETHING ELSE I MUST TELL YOU...

IT ALL STARTED WHEN I CLIMBED OUT THE REFRESHER WINDOW ONTO THE LEDGE...

WHAT?

WHAT?!

END

ONE WEEK AGO...

OKAY, WORD HAS IT THAT BOBA FETT HASN'T ARRIVED YET BECAUSE HE GOT SIDETRACKED GOING AFTER A PERSONAL BOUNTY.

REALLY?

IS SOMETHING WRONG?

NO, GO AHEAD. PLEASE CONTINUE.

ANYWAY, APPARENTLY THESE TWO GUYS ALMOST LEFT HIM FOR DEAD ON YAVIN 4 SOME TIME AGO, AND HE'S GONE OFF TO TAKE CARE OF THEM BEFORE THEY HAVE A CHANCE TO SLIP AWAY AGAIN.

REALLY?!

SORRY ABOUT THAT. I'VE GOT SOME PRETTY EXPENSIVE CARGO.

I'M SURE YOU DO.

WELL... EVERYTHING SEEMS TO BE IN ORDER. HAVE A GOOD TRIP.

THANKS. HEY, GLAD TO SEE YOU GUYS MADE IT OFF OF CLOUD CITY.

WELL IT WAS A BIT HAIRY AT FIRST, BUT BINK AND I... AYE AYE AYE...

OH, MAN, THAT--

FIVE DAYS LATER.

VICTIMS OF THE ALMIGHTY SARLACC...

HEY, YOU HEAR THAT?

YEAH. WHAT'S THAT LIGHT?

JABBA, THIS IS YOUR LAST CHANCE.

CAN YOU SEE WHAT'S GOING ON UP THERE?

NOT REALLY, BUT IT LOOKS LIKE SOMEBODY'S ABOUT TO TAKE A SWAN DIVE. SO BRACE YOURSELF.

LOOK OUT!

HERE COMES ANOTHER ONE!

HEY, I THINK I SEE LANDO'S FOOT!

OH, MAN, THIS IS MAKING ME SICK.

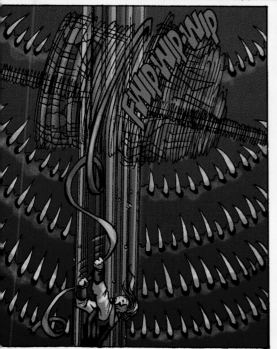

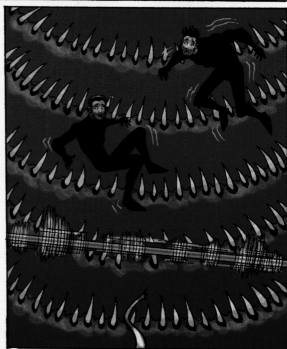

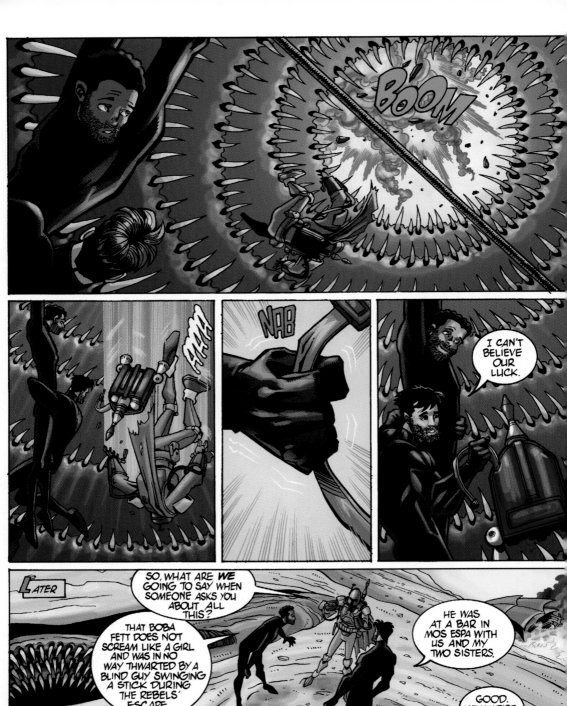

ONCE BITTEN

MAKE YOURSELF AT HOME.

HOW DID YOU PUT IT? "AVOID ANY IMPERIAL ENTANGLEMENTS..." WAS IT?

WELL THAT WAS ABOUT AS "ENTANGLED" AS THEY COME! I HOPE YOU'RE HERE TO THANK ME!

YOU'RE BEING WELL PAID FOR ALL YOUR EFFORTS, CAPTAIN.

DO YOU KNOW WHAT BLASTING OUT OF THERE LIKE THAT DOES TO MY REPUTATION?

NOT TO MENTION HAVING TO RUN FROM THE IMPERIALS?

PEOPLE ARE GOING TO THINK I'M IN TROUBLE!

AREN'T YOU?

EVEN THE VILEST OF VILLAINS ARE WELL OFF TO KNOW WHEN THEY'RE OUTMATCHED. I REMEMBER BACK WHEN I WAS JUST A PADAWAN...

SHE HAD YOU BOTH ON THE ROPES AND JUST UP AND LEFT?

I WOULD LIKE TO THINK SHE THOUGHT US TOO POWER-FUL.

AURRA AND I WOULD INDEED BOTH LIVE TO MEET AGAIN.

JEDI ASSASSIN?! LOOK, I AIN'T THE BIGGEST BELIEVER IN ALL THAT KOOKY MYSTICISM, BUT EVEN I KNOW THAT JEDI DON'T DIE EASY.

EXACTLY. BUT AURRA SING WAS ONCE A JEDI HER-SELF.

ALL RIGHT, ENOUGH WITH THE HISTORY LESSON. WHAT'D YOU COME UP HERE FOR, ANYWAY?

DO YOU HAVE A TRAINING REMOTE ON BOARD?

I WOULD LIKE TO BEGIN THE BOY'S LIGHT-SABER LESSON.

WHATEVER. ASK CHEWIE. HE JUST WENT BACK THERE TO WARM UP THE HOLO-CHESS TABLE.

ONCE THE REST OF THIS LITTLE CAKE WALK IS OVER AND WE GET PAID, CHEWIE AND I'LL BE IN THE CLEAR.

THERE'LL BE NO REASON FOR US TO HAVE TO TURN TAIL AND RUN FROM ANYONE ANYMORE.

END.

THEY'VE ENTERED THE BASE.

NO MATTER HOW MANY HE REPELS, HE'S FAILING. MORE COME.

THIS IS HIS DUTY--HE WILL DIE SO NO MORE OF HIS CHARGES DO.

HE'LL DO ANYTHING FOR THEIR SAFETY.

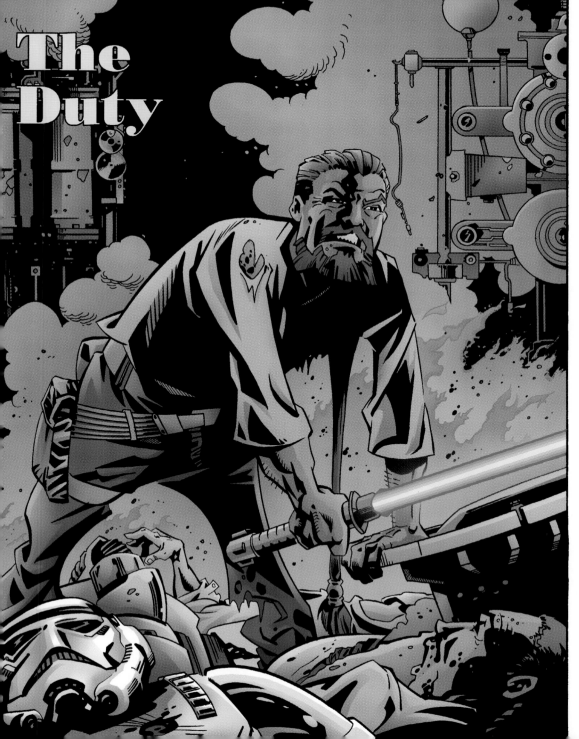

The Duty

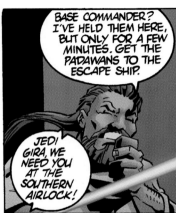

BASE COMMANDER? I'VE HELD THEM HERE, BUT ONLY FOR A FEW MINUTES. GET THE PADAWANS TO THE ESCAPE SHIP.

JEDI GIRA, WE NEED YOU AT THE SOUTHERN AIRLOCK!

THE LAST OF THE PADAWAN LEARNERS IN THE REPUBLIC. AND VADER IS HERE TO FINISH THEM OFF.

HE JUST NEEDS TIME TO GET THE LAST SURVIVORS TO SAFETY. TO AN ESCAPE VESSEL.

THEY SENT IN STORMTROOPERS FIRST. HE'S BEEN HOLDING THEM BACK BUT THERE ARE TOO MANY.

BUT VADER WILL BE COMING SOON TO DO HIS DUTY. THEY'RE ALMOST OUT OF TIME.

VVMMM

COMMANDER! THEY'RE OUTSIDE THE AIRLOCK.

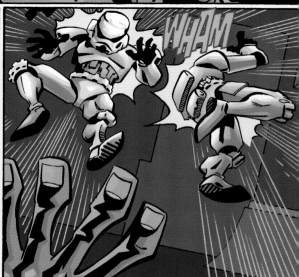

WHAM

YOU SHOULD HAVE WARNED ME THEY WERE HERE...

SORRY. THEY... MUST HAVE MOVED. WE JUST GOT WORD. VADER'S ENTERED THE STATION.

HE'S ABOUT SEVEN HUNDRED METERS FROM YOU.

AT LEAST HE CAN DO HIS DUTY.

THAT'S ALL THAT MATTERS. A JEDI KNIGHT IS ONE WHO SERVES.

COMMANDER, YOU ARE MANNING SECURITY CAMS, YES?

I AM.

SO... WHY WERE THESE MEN SHOT IN THE BACK? YOU COULD HAVE WARNED THEM...

VMMMM

FEAR LEADS TO ANGER, ANGER LEADS TO HATE...

...HATE LEADS--

VADER IS SO MUCH STRONGER, MORE RUTHLESS AND RELENTLESS THAN GIRA. HE CAN FEEL HIS CALM GIVE WAY TO PANIC.

I CAN FEEL THE FEAR. THE HATE. YOU ARE CLOSE TO THE DARK SIDE NOW.

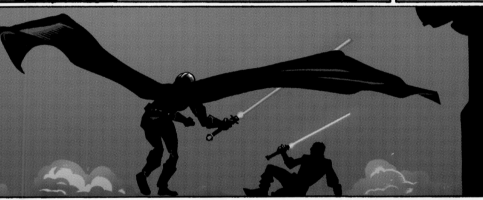

IT IS OVER. BUT YOU DO NOT *HAVE* TO DIE.

MY MASTER HAS USE FOR ALL. JOIN US, AND I WILL SPARE THE PADAWANS.

GIRA STARES DEATH IN THE FACE. THIS IS HIS DUTY.

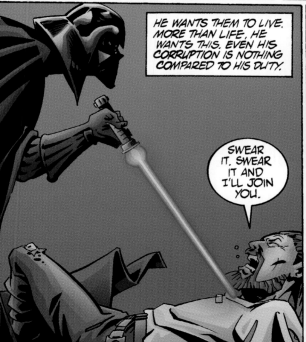

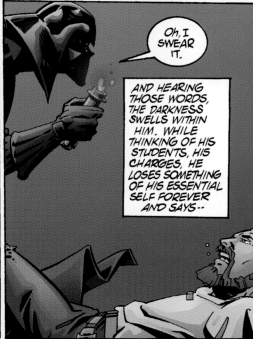

WITNESS THE TRUE COST OF YOUR LOYALTY.

GIRA FEELS THE COLD DESPAIR SETTLE INTO HIS BONES. HE KNOWS HE WILL NEVER AGAIN ESCAPE THE FEAR AND ANGER. NEVER RECEIVE ONE MOMENT'S RESPITE.

THIS IS THE ESCAPE SHIP YOUR PADAWANS ARE ON. THEY HAVE FLED THIS FACILITY.

AS HE SEES THE SHIP ROCKET TO SAFETY, HE PRAYS THAT SOMEHOW, SOME WAY, IT WAS A PRICE WORTH PAYING.

GIRA? ARE YOU THERE?

EVEN THOUGH HE WILL, MUST, BECOME THEIR ENEMY ONE DAY, FOR NOW, THEY ARE SAFE. HIS FIRST, MOST IMPORTANT DUTY IS DONE.

YES COMMANDER. WHAT IS IT?

I MUST SPEAK WITH LORD VADER, JEDI.

COMMANDER, ARE THE EXPLOSIVES YOU SET ON THE ESCAPE VESSEL CHARGED?

YES, LORD VADER.

PROCEED.

WHAT? I SWORE TO SERVE YOU! YOU SWORE TO ME!

YOUR BASE COMMANDER SWORE ALLEGIANCE ONCE HE SAW THAT YOU WOULD FAIL TO REPEL US.

UNLIKE YOU, HE PUT NO PRICE ON HIS SERVICE. WHICH IS HOW I AMBUSHED YOU WITH SUCH EASE.

AND MY PROMISE IS NOTHING WEIGHED AGAINST MY DUTY TO MY MASTER.

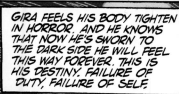

GIRA FEELS HIS BODY TIGHTEN IN HORROR. AND HE KNOWS THAT NOW HE'S SWORN TO THE DARK SIDE HE WILL FEEL THIS WAY FOREVER. THIS IS HIS DESTINY. FAILURE OF DUTY, FAILURE OF SELF.

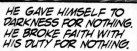

HE GAVE HIMSELF TO DARKNESS FOR NOTHING. HE BROKE FAITH WITH HIS DUTY FOR NOTHING.

WHY?! IF YOU WANTED THEM DEAD, WHY NOT KILL ME? WHY THE GAME? WHY DID YOU WANT ME?

BECAUSE IT WAS EASIER THIS WAY. BECAUSE MY MASTER PREFERS TO POSSESS RATHER THAN DESTROY.

BUT YOU SERVED ONLY TO SAVE YOUR STUDENTS.

THAT IS IMPURE SERVICE AND UNWORTHY OF THE MASTER.

END

Star Wars: Tales #11 / COVER BY
KILIAN PLUNKETT, COLORS JASON HVAM

Star Wars: Tales #12 / cover by John McCrea and Jimmy Palmiotti, colors Dan Jackson